Primary School
Chinese
Character Book 2

Written by
Marcus Reoch

Primary School Chinese Character Book 2 accompanies Primary School Chinese Textbook 2. It is aimed at young students studying Mandarin Chinese at a basic level, but is also a useful tool for older learners. This book is fully aligned to Primary School Chinese Textbook 2 and will enable the student to revise and practise the fundamentals of Chinese characters.

Chinese Character Book 2:

♦ contains tracing grids to ensure accuracy in Chinese character writing.

♦ includes blank grids for further writing practice.

♦ has a wide range of exercises to test students on characters that appear throughout the course.

♦ is a fun and motivational tool to accompany Primary School Chinese Textbook 2 and e-portal.

In addition, the characters included in the book follow the specifications for the Independent Schools Examinations Board (ISEB) Level 1 Common Entrance exam (launched in 2012).

Trace the Chinese characters below!

qiǎo
kè
lì

xīn

bù

mǎi

Now practise on your own!

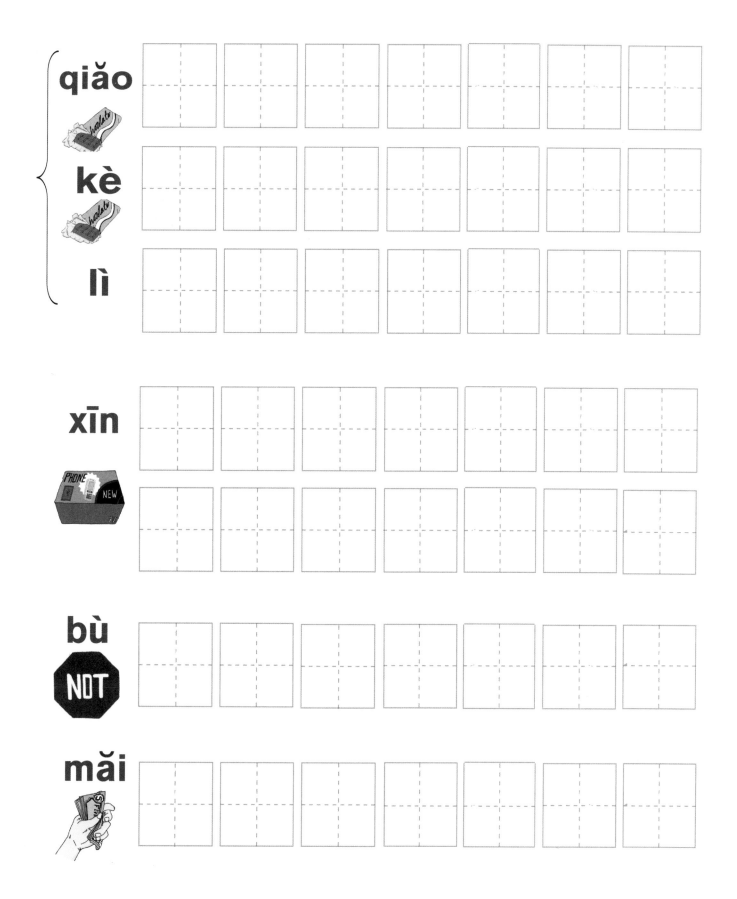

qiǎo

kè

lì

xīn

bù

mǎi

Let's play Battleships! Find the characters in the grid below and write down the correct reference!

	A	**B**	**C**
1	姐姐	十一	两点
2	好	吃	中国
3	不	英国	新
4	手	笔	毛衣
5	帽子	水	买

to eat   **B2**

China   _____

pen   _____

to buy   _____

hat   _____

new   _____

big sister   _____

Complete the short sentences. Write the correct Chinese characters in the empty boxes!

Dad 爸爸 wants to buy ☐ some chocolate ☐ ☐ ☐

and some water ☐ . Little sister ☐ ☐ does not ☐ like

chocolate but she loves hamburgers ☐ ☐ ☐ ! Today I

am going to buy ☐ a new ☐ hat ☐ ☐ - I hope that my

Mum ☐ ☐ likes it.

3

Look at the pictures, then write and trace the correct Chinese characters in the boxes below!

bag =包 ruler =尺 book=书 pen=笔 new =新 not new =不新

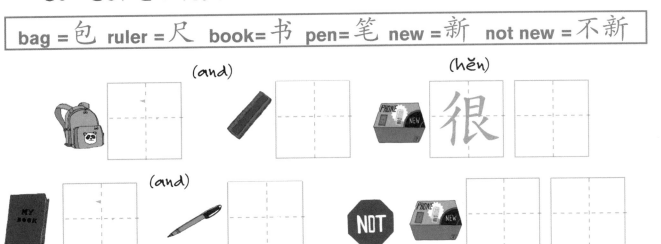

(and)

(hěn)

很

(and)

Look at the pictures, then write and trace the correct Chinese characters in the boxes below!

hat =帽子 mobile phone=手机 big =大 not small =不小

(hěn)

很

机

NOT

What are the sisters buying? Write and trace the correct characters in the boxes provided!

Big sister=姐姐 Little sister=妹妹 buy=买 tea=茶 shoes= 鞋子

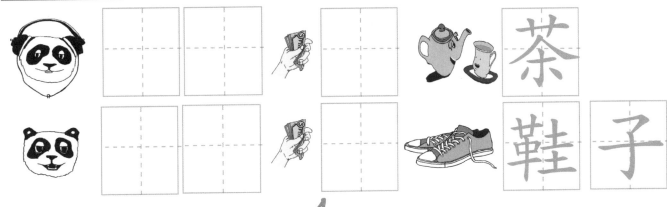

茶

鞋子

Trace the Chinese characters below!

jiā

kè

tīng

zài

shā

fā

Now practise on your own!

Chapter 2
Inside my House

Count the number of objects in the house and then write the correct number using characters in the boxes provided!

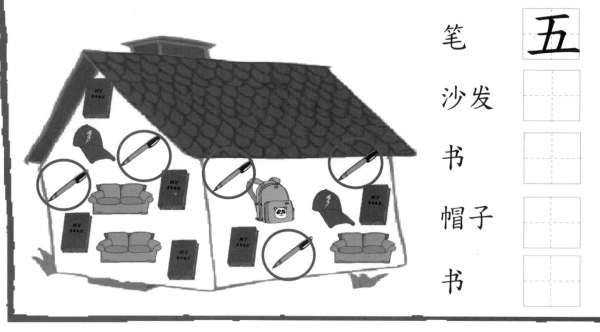

笔	五
沙发	
书	
帽子	
书	

Select! Read the short sentences, then select the correct Chinese characters to match the **bold** words.

Little sister is in the **sitting room**.
(客厅) (妹妹) 毛衣   姐姐

The **book is in** the kitchen at **home**.
书 大 笔 两 家 在

China is **not big**.
大 美国 不 四 中国

The **sofa is in** the **sitting room**.
客厅 十点 在 好 沙发

Mum is **not** going to **Beijing**.
北京 包 不 水 九 妈妈

The **black jumper** is at **home**.
毛衣 黑 红 绿 家 沙发

7

Who? Where? Look at the pictures, then write and trace the correct Chinese characters in the boxes below!

Teacher=老师 Dad=爸爸 is in=在 sitting room=客厅 kitchen=厨房

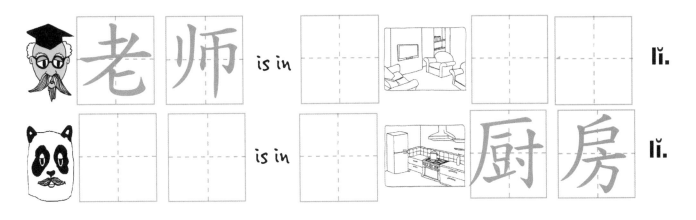

老师 is in [　] lǐ.

[　] is in 厨房 lǐ.

Look at the pictures, then write and trace the correct Chinese characters in the boxes below!

jumper=毛衣 sofa=沙发 is in=在 sitting room=客厅 bedroom=卧室

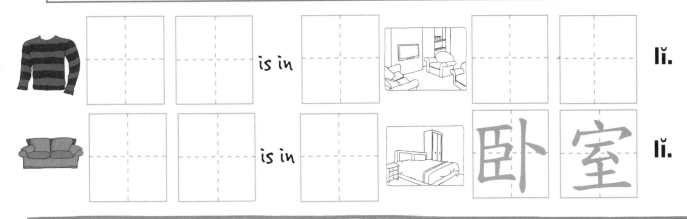

is in [　] lǐ.

is in 卧室 lǐ.

Look at the pictures, then write and trace the correct Chinese characters in the boxes below!

I=我 chair=椅子 am at/is in=在 home=家 bathroom=浴室

 我 am at [　]

 椅子 is in [　] 浴室 lǐ.

8

Trace the Chinese characters below!

Now practise on your own!

niú

ròu

niú

năi

zuò

fàn

dāo

10

Look at the pictures, then complete the answers using characters! Remember to trace over the grey ones!

1.

水

2.

3.

4.

面

5.

6.

Complete the missing characters in this short story about Candy. Remember to trace the grey ones!

I 我 like to eat ☐ beef ☐☐ , bread 面 ☐

and hamburgers ☐☐☐ . I like to drink ☐ tea 茶

and apple juice 苹果汁 . My little brother ☐☐

likes tea 茶 but he doesn't like orange juice 橙汁 .

11

Look at the pictures, write and trace the correct Chinese characters in the boxes below!

Big dragon=大龙　He=他　eat=吃　beef=牛肉　noodles=面条

 龙

He 他 面 条

Look at the pictures, then write and trace the correct Chinese characters in the boxes below!

Little dragon=小龙　She=她　drink=喝　milk=牛奶　water=水

 龙

She 她

Look at the pictures, then write and trace the correct Chinese characters in the boxes below!

You=你　teacher =老师　I=我　cook= 做饭　do not cook=不做饭

You 你

 老师

I 我

Trace the Chinese characters below!

Hàn

yǔ

kè

běn

yǒu

méi

Now practise on your own!

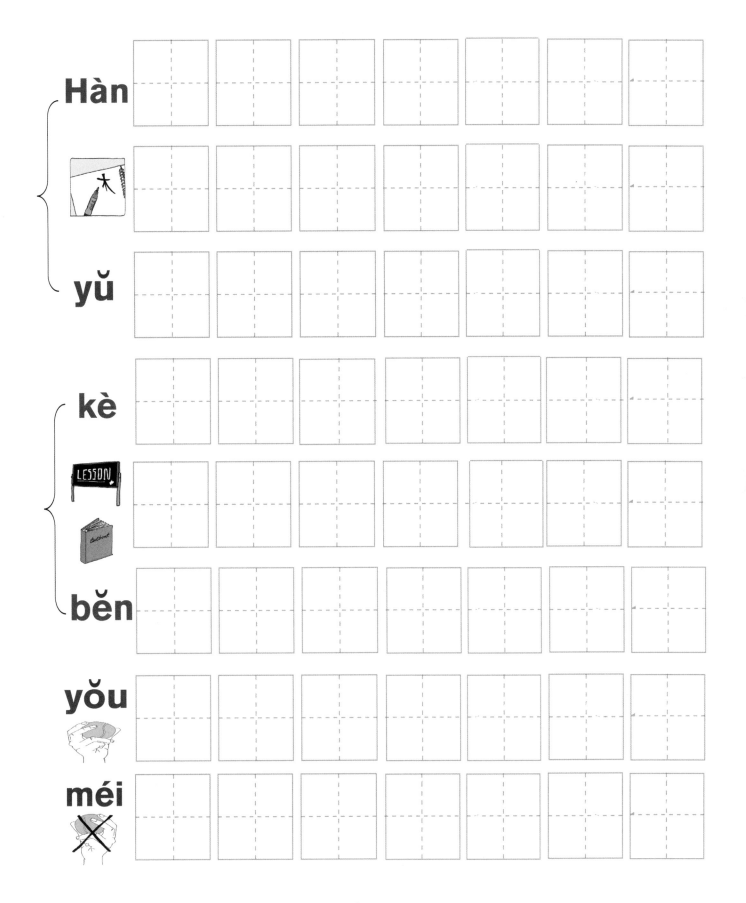

Hàn

yǔ

kè

běn

yǒu

méi

汉语课本有没汉语课本有没汉语课本有没汉语课本有没汉语课本有没汉语课本有没汉语课本有
汉语课本有没汉语课本有没汉语课本有没汉语课本有没汉语课本有没汉语课本有没汉语课本有
汉语课本有没汉语课本有没汉语课本有没汉语课本有没汉语课本有没汉语课本有没汉语课本有

Chapter 4
My School

Look at the books, then write/trace the correct subject title, using characters, on the covers!

| 科学 | | 英语 | 数学 |

| science | Chinese | English | maths |

Match the numbers to the Chinese characters, then translate them into English. Check out p.42 if you need some help!

1	2	3	4	5	6	7
数学	课	作业	汉语	英语	课本	考试

a) 1, 7   _maths exam_ _____

b) 4, 3   _____

c) 5, 6   _____

d) 4, 2   _____

e) 1,6   _____

textbook

15

Mike's got a Chinese exam today! Write and trace the correct Chinese characters in the boxes below!

Chinese=汉语 English=英语 textbook=课本 exam=考试 homework=作业

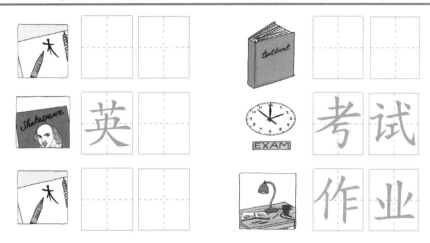

Let's write some plurals! Trace the correct Chinese characters in the boxes below!

We=我们 You (plural)=你们 are= 是 teachers=老师 students=学生

We 我 们 are 是 老 师

You 你 们 are 是 学 生

Practise writing **yǒu** and/or **méiyǒu**. Write and trace the correct Chinese characters in the boxes below!

have/don't have=有/没有 Chinese=汉语 science=科学 lesson=课 homework=作业

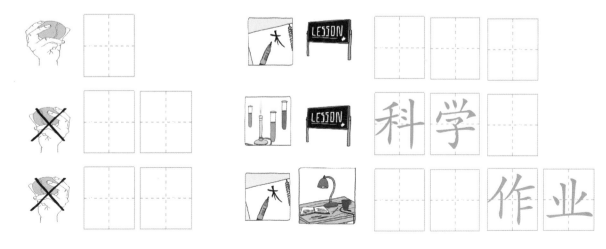

16

Trace the Chinese characters below!

jī — 鸡

ròu — 肉

qì — 汽

shuǐ — 水

xǐ — 喜

huan — 欢

ma? — 吗

Now practise on your own!

Chapter 5
I like

Food and drink review! Match the pictures to the correct Chinese characters!

Complete the missing characters in this short story about the teacher. Remember to trace the grey ones!

The teacher 老师 likes ____ chicken ____ ,

chips 薯条 and fizzy drinks ____ . She 她 and her

big sister ____ want to go to Beijing ____ to eat

noodles 面条 and drink ____ tea 茶 . They 她们

both don't like ____ chocolate ____ and

Coca Cola ____ because they are too sweet!

That's tasty! Write and trace the correct Chinese characters in the boxes below!

beef=牛肉 fizzy drinks=汽水 chicken=鸡肉 tasty =好吃/好喝 not=不

TASTY!

TASTY!

NOT TASTY!

NOT

I like...? Write and trace the correct Chinese characters in the boxes below!

I=我 He=他 likes/doesn't like=喜欢/不喜欢 chicken=鸡肉 chips=薯条 tea=茶

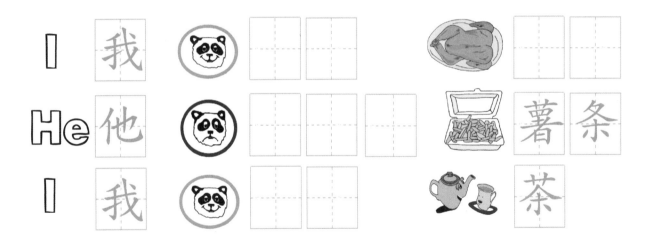

I 我

He 他

I 我

薯 条

茶

Let's practise writing 吗! Write and trace the correct Chinese characters in the boxes below!

Do you like China?=你喜欢中国吗？ Do you like Beijing?=你喜欢北京吗？

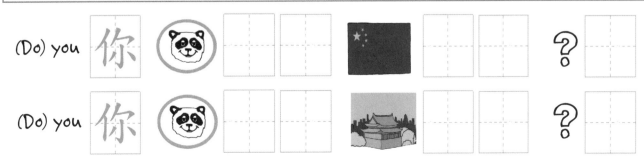

(Do) you 你

(Do) you 你

Trace the Chinese characters below!

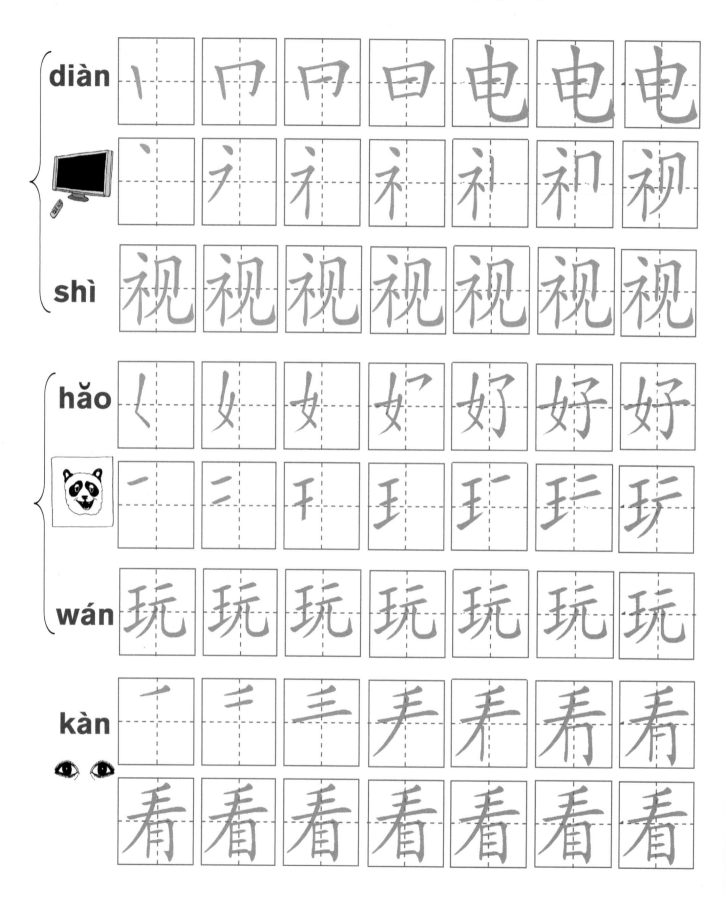

diàn
shì
hǎo
wán
kàn

好玩看电视好玩看电视好玩看电视好玩看电视好玩看电视好玩看电视好玩看电视好玩看电视
视好玩看电视好玩看电视好玩看电视好玩看电视好玩看电视好玩看电视好玩看电视好玩看电视
视好玩看电视好玩看电视好玩看电视好玩看电视好玩看电视好玩看电视好玩看电视好玩看电视

Chapter 6
My Hobbies

Now practise on your own!

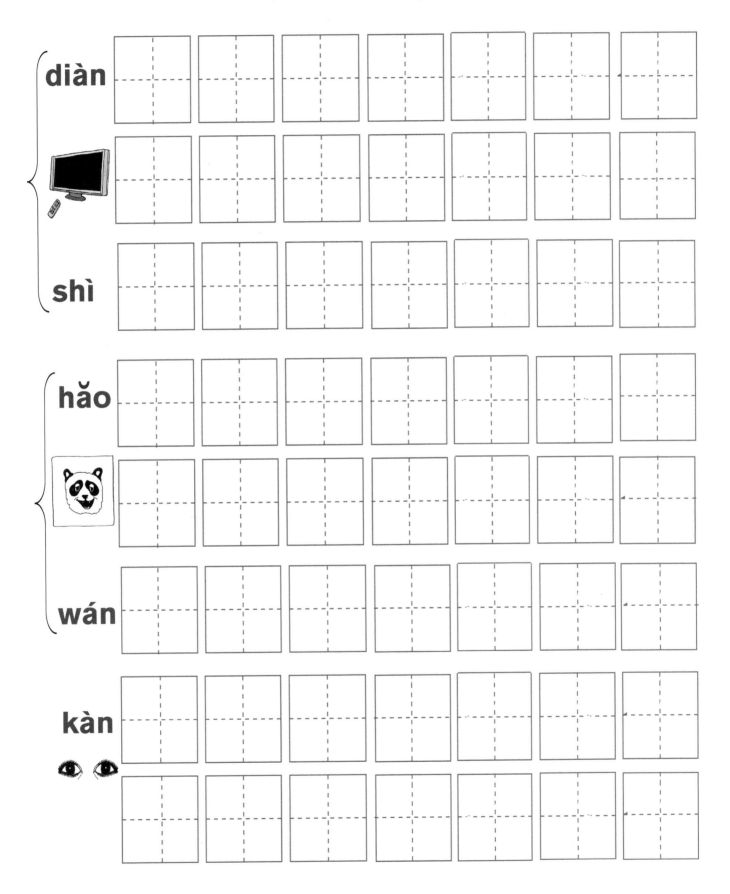

Object review! Link the pictures to the correct
Chinese characters and then complete your own version!

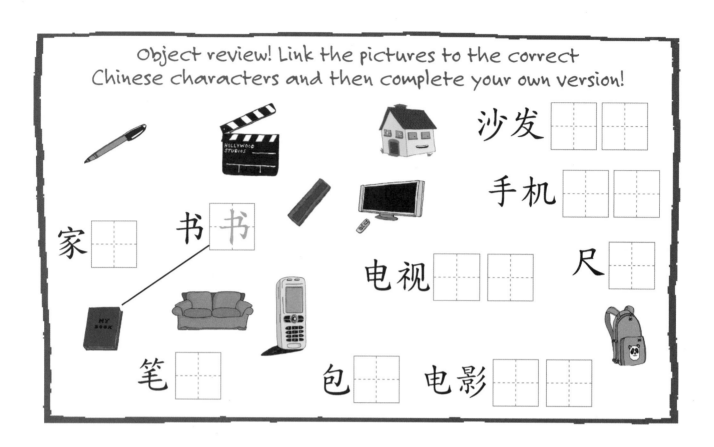

Select! Read the short sentences, then select the
correct Chinese characters to match the **bold** words.

He thinks the **film** is **funny**.

（电影） 书 妹妹 姐姐 （好玩）

We **don't have** a **TV**.

小 客厅 没有 电视 牛奶

Big brother has a **hat**.

哥哥 有 喜 弟弟 帽子 没有

I **like** to **watch** cowboy **films**.

喜欢 你 看 吃 沙发 电影

She is **not** buying **chicken**.

大 哥哥 不 牛肉 鸡肉

The **TV is in** the **sitting room**.

买 电视 十 在 新 客厅

Look at the pictures, then write and trace the correct Chinese characters in the boxes below!

TV = 电视 mobile phone= 手机 is in= 在 bathroom= 浴室 kitchen= 厨房

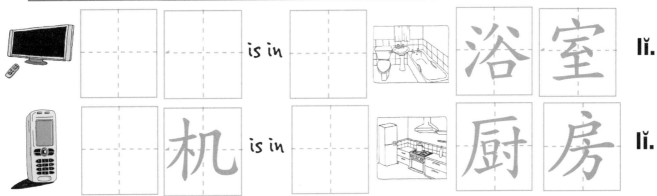

is in 浴室 lǐ.

机 is in 厨房 lǐ.

The film is funny! Write and trace the correct Chinese characters in the boxes below!

film= 电影 textbook= 课本 science= 科学 funny= 好玩 interesting= 有意思 boring= 无聊

影 hěn

hěn 意思

科学 hěn 无聊

Who is doing what? Write and trace the correct Chinese characters in the boxes below!

We= 我们 She= 她 use the computer= 用电脑 surfs the net= 上网

We 我们

use the computer.

用 脑

She 她

surfs the net.

上网

Trace the Chinese characters below!

pǎo							
bù							
zú							
qiú							
yào							

Now practise on your own!

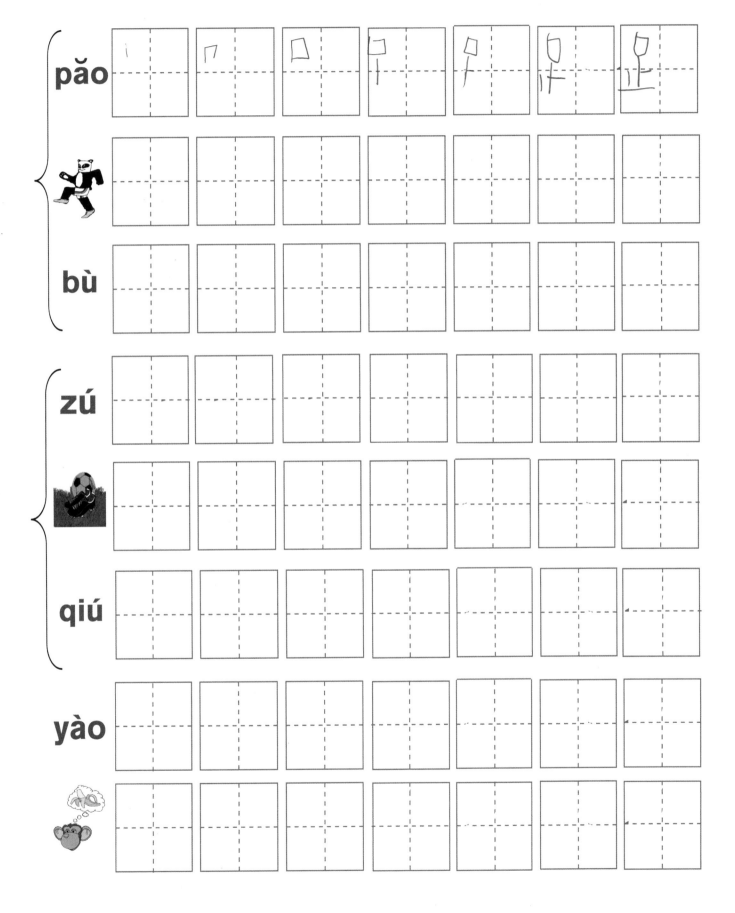

Sports/activity practice! Write the correct verbs in the boxes provided. Don't forget to trace the grey ones!

to run

打

to play ping pong

打 兵 兵 球

to cook

to play tennis

打 网

to play football

踢 足 球

to swim

游 泳

Complete the missing characters in this short story about the students. Remember to trace the grey ones!

It's 2 o'clock ⬜⬜⬜ ! It's time for the students 学 生

to play football 踢 ⬜⬜ . They 他 们 are having ⬜

a Chinese ⬜⬜ lesson ⬜ and then they have ⬜ an

exam 考 试 . Later on, they want ⬜ to go running ⬜⬜

and then go for a swim 游 泳 but the teacher 老 师 does

not want ⬜⬜ them to be outside - the weather isn't good ⬜ .

27

What does teacher like? Write and trace the correct Chinese characters in the boxes below!

Teacher=老师 I=我 like/don't like= 喜欢/不喜欢 football =足球 tennis=网球

What about little dragon? Write and trace the correct Chinese characters in the boxes below!

Xiǎolóng=小龙 You=你 like/don't like=喜欢/不喜欢 sports=运动 P.E=体育

Who wants what? Write and trace the correct Chinese characters in the boxes below!

We=我们 She=她 want/not want=要/不要 play football=踢足球 cook=做饭

28

Trace the Chinese characters below!

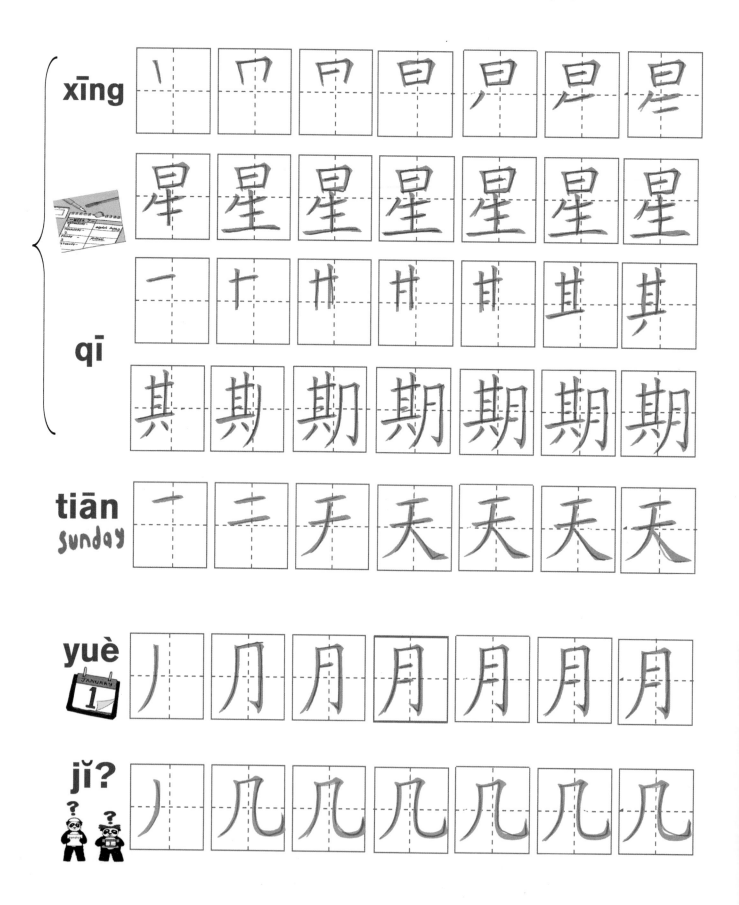

xīng

qī

tiān
sunday

yuè

jǐ?

Now practise on your own!

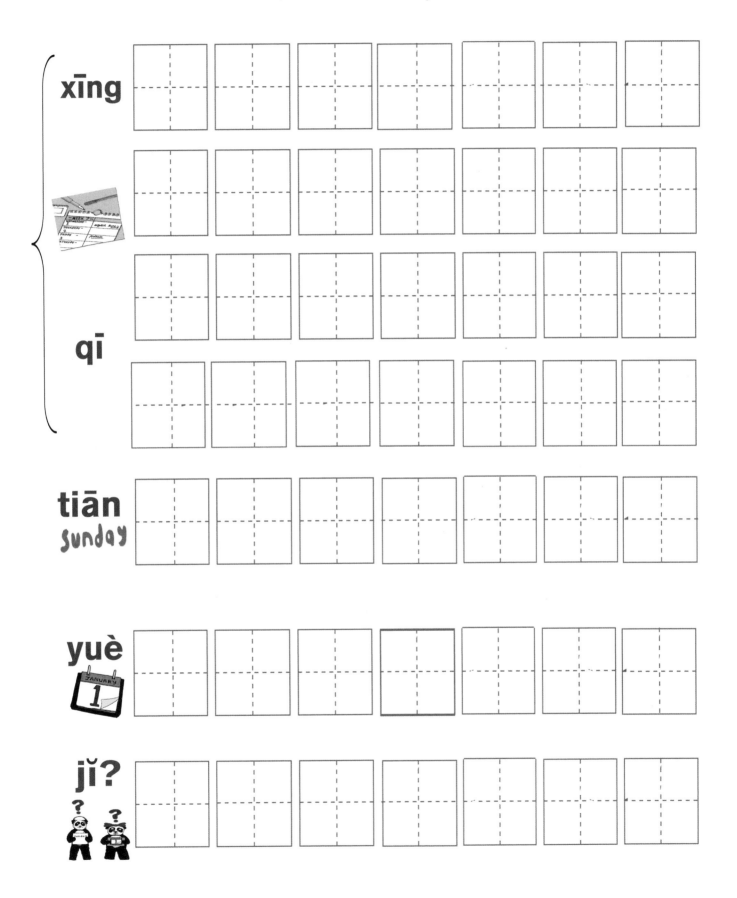

xīng

qī

tiān
sunday

yuè

jǐ?

Let's play Battleships! Find the characters in the grid below, then write down the correct reference!

	A	B	C
1	星期六	星期几	星期天
2	十点	星期三	十二月
3	五月	几点了	六点
4	八点	几月	星期二
5	两点	七点	星期一

Tuesday **C4**

Which month is it? _____

2 o'clock _____

December _____

Saturday _____

8 o'clock _____

What day is it? _____

May _____

Time review! Link the pictures/words to the correct Chinese character and then complete your own version.

星期五

August

七月

September   3 o' clock   Friday

July

四月   星期一

八月

三点   Thursday   九月

Monday

9 o' clock

九点   April   星期四

31

Questions about time! Write and trace the correct Chinese characters in the boxes below!

What day is it?=星期几？ Which month is it?=几月？ What time is it?=几点了？

What day is it?

Which month is it?

What time is it?

What are you doing on Sunday? Write and trace the correct Chinese characters in the boxes below!

You=你　He=他　Sunday=星期天　Tuesday=星期二　run=跑步　swim=游泳

You 你 Sunday

He 他 Tuesday

游 泳

What do you in February? Write and trace the correct Chinese characters in the boxes below!

I=我　She=她　February=二月　October=十月　cook=做饭　watch TV=看电视

I 我 February

She 她 October

Trace the Chinese characters below!

qǐ

chuáng

shàng

xué

zǎo

fàn

33

Now practise on your own!

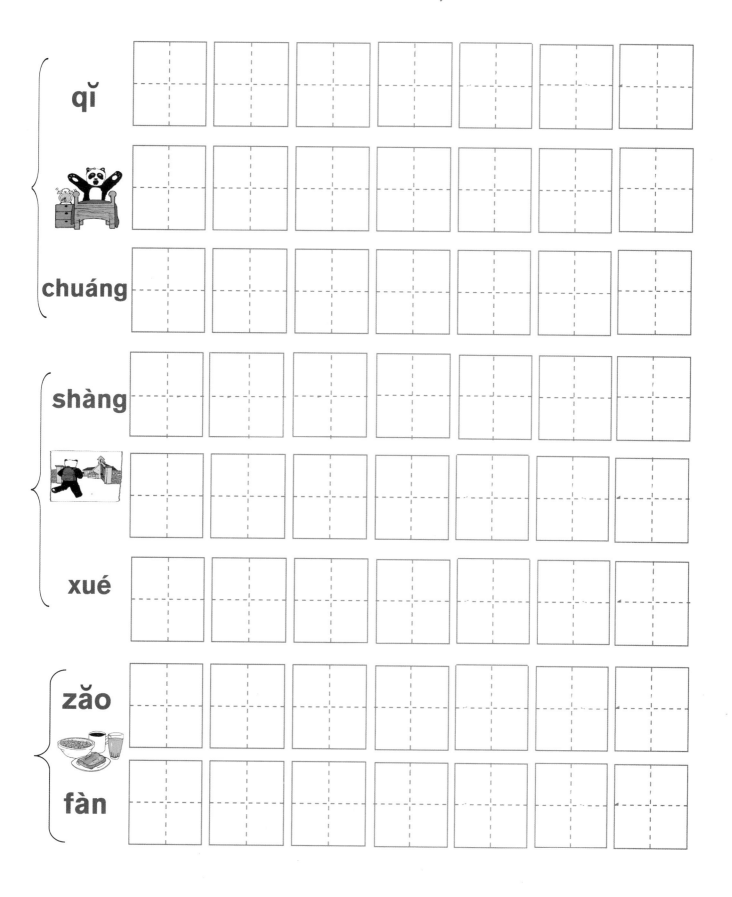

qǐ

chuáng

shàng

xué

zǎo

fàn

起床上学早饭起床上学早饭起床上学早饭起床上学早饭起床上学早饭起床上学早饭起床上学早
起床上学早饭起床上学早饭起床上学早饭起床上学早饭起床上学早饭起床上学早饭起床上学早
起床上学早饭起床上学早饭起床上学早饭起床上学早饭起床上学早饭起床上学早饭起床上学早

Chapter 9
My Day

Match the numbers to the Chinese characters,
then translate them into correct English sentences.

1	2	3	4	5	6
上学	八点	七点	起床	我	做饭

7	8	9	10	11	12
哥哥	踢足球	妹妹	三点	爸爸	看电视

a) 5, 10, 8   *I play football at 3 o'clock.*

b) 11, 3, 4   _____

c) 7, 10, 12   _____

d) 9, 2, 1   _____

e) 5, 3, 6   _____

Complete the missing characters in this short story about
the student. Remember to trace the grey ones!

Today is Wednesday ☐☐☐ . The student ☐ 生

wakes up ☐☐ at 7 o'clock ☐☐ and then has her

breakfast ☐☐ . It's 8 o'clock ☐☐☐ ! It's time to

go to school ☐☐ - her first lesson is Chinese ☐☐ which

she 她 really likes ☐☐ because the teacher 老师 is

funny ☐☐ and her textbook is interesting ☐ 意思 .

What time does Dad...? Write and trace the correct Chinese characters in the boxes below!

| Dad=爸爸 | Mum=妈妈 | What time?=几点 | get up=起床 | go to school=上学 |

What time do you..? Write and trace the correct Chinese characters in the boxes below!

| You=你 | Teacher=老师 | 5/2 o'clock=五/两点 | play tennis =打网球 | surf the net =上网 |

You 你 [05:00] 打 网

老 师 [02:00] [WWW.] 网

What's for breakfast? Write and trace the correct Chinese characters in the boxes below!

| breakfast=早饭 | supper=晚饭 | I=我 | he=他 | eat=吃 | drink=喝 | beef=牛肉 | milk=牛奶 |

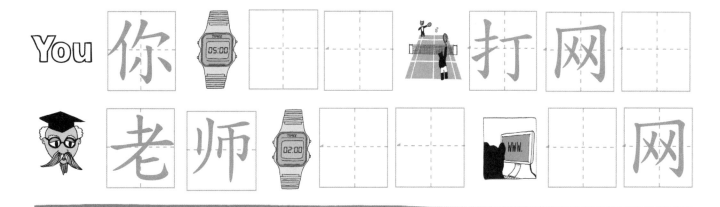

breakfast   I 我

晚   he 他

supper

36

Trace the Chinese characters below!

jià

qī

qù

Cháng

Chéng

Now practise on your own!

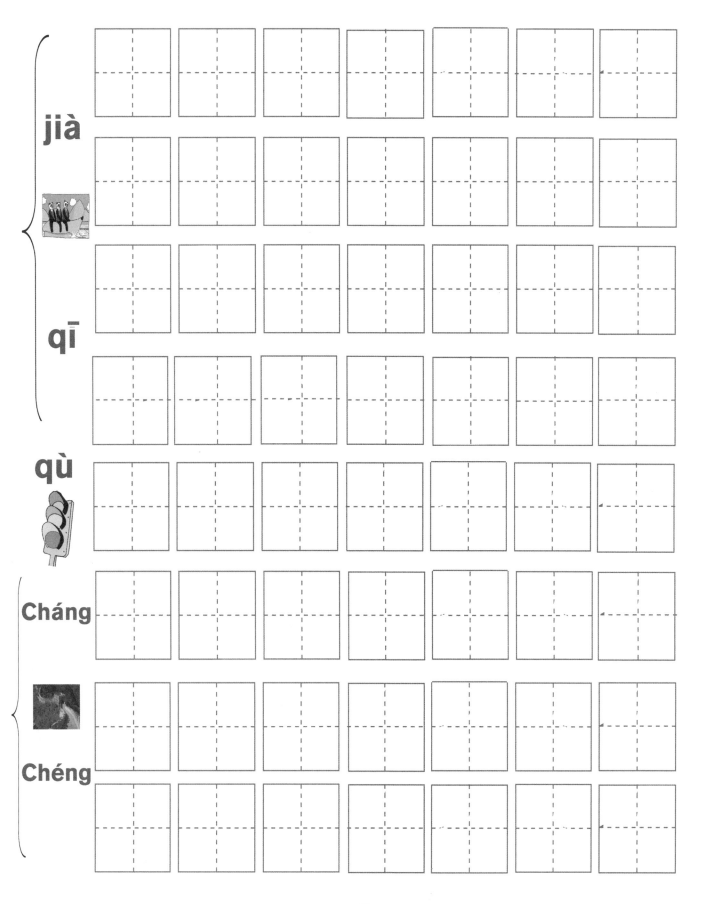

jià

qī

qù

Cháng

Chéng

Fill in the grids!

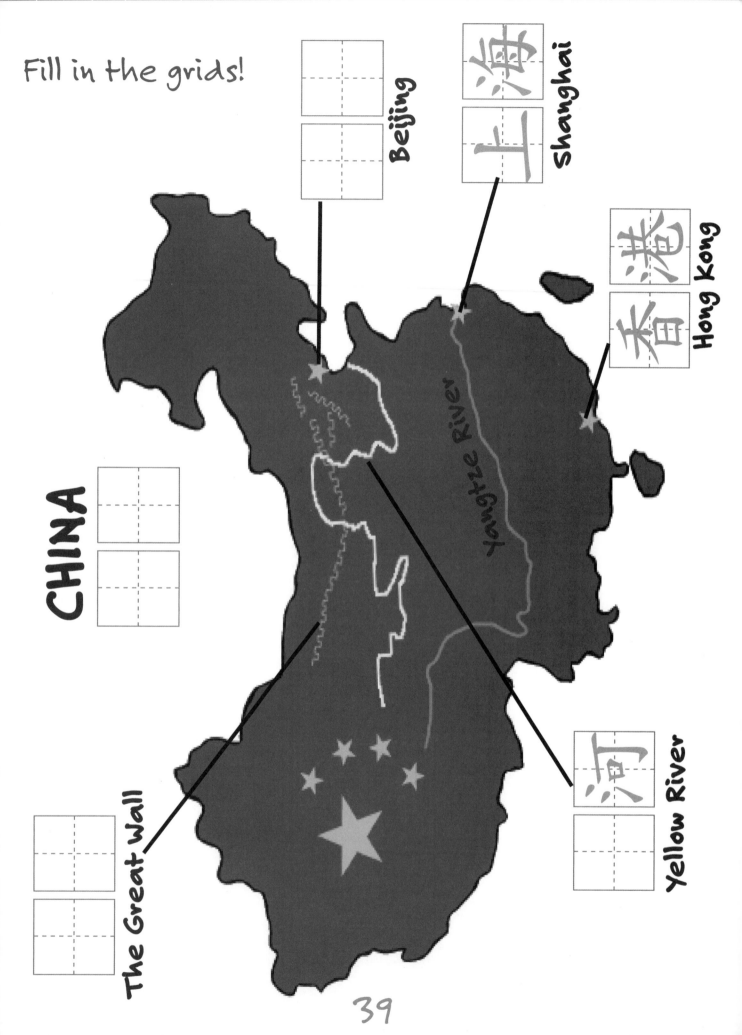

Beijing

上海 Shanghai

香港 Hong Kong

CHINA

Yangtze River

河 Yellow River

The Great Wall

39

Who likes holidays? Write and trace the correct Chinese characters in the boxes below!

Dàlóng=大龙　You=你　to like/not like=喜欢/不喜欢　holidays=假期　beach=海滩

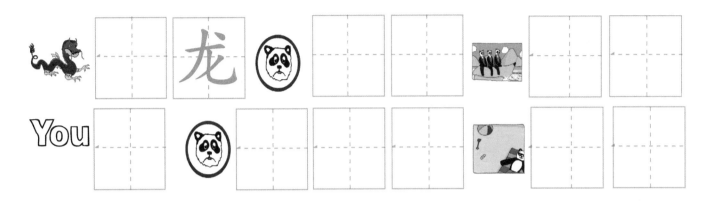

Who is going where? Write and trace the correct Chinese characters in the boxes below!

We=我们　Little brother=弟弟　go=去　hotel=饭店　The Great Wall=长城

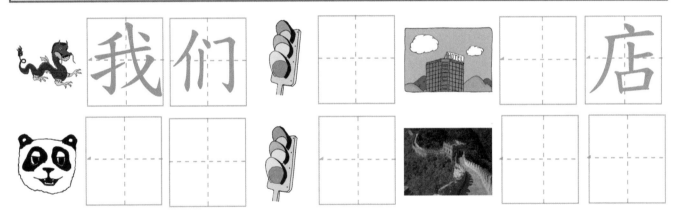

Who else... and where? Write and trace the correct Chinese characters in the boxes below!

Teacher=老师　Big sister=姐姐　go=去　Shanghai=上海　Beijing=北京

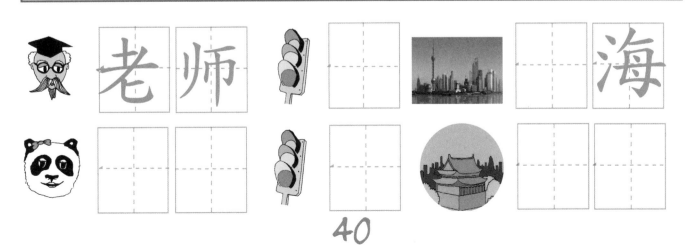

40

QUICK SEARCH

SHOPPING

手机	mobile phone	新	new
体恤衫	T-shirt	美丽	beautiful
巧克力	chocolate	便宜	cheap

你买什么？　　What are you buying?
我买汉堡包。　I am buying a hamburger.

INSIDE THE HOUSE

家	house/home	沙发	sofa
卧室	bedroom	桌子	table
浴室	bathroom	椅子	chair
客厅	sitting room	床	bed
厨房	kitchen		

爸爸在哪里？　　Where is Dad?
爸爸在客厅里。　Dad is in the sitting room.

WHAT'S COOKING?

鸡蛋	eggs	牛奶	milk	刀	knife
面包	bread	橙汁	orange juice	叉子	fork
牛肉	beef	苹果汁	apple juice	勺子	spoon
				筷子	chopsticks

你们做什么？　What are you doing?
我们做饭。　　We are cooking food.

41

AT SCHOOL

课	lesson
考试	exam
课本	textbook
作业	homework
学生	student
老师	teacher

SUBJECTS

汉语	Chinese
英语	English
数学	maths
科学	science

MORE FOOD & DRINK

鸡肉	chicken
薯条	chips
汽水	fizzy drinks
咖啡	coffee

LIKE AND DISLIKE

他喜欢鸡肉。

He likes chicken.

我不喜欢咖啡。

I don't like coffee.

TASTY...

薯条很好吃。 Chips are tasty.

汽水很好喝。 Fizzy drinks are tasty.

HOBBIES

看电视	watch TV
看电影	watch a film
用电脑	use the computer
上网	surf the net

有意思	interesting
好玩	funny
无聊	boring

弟弟喜欢看电视。 Little brother likes watching TV.

书很有意思。 The book is interesting.

电影很无聊。 The film is boring.

SPORTS

球	ball	跑步	running
足球	football	游泳	swimming
体育	P.E	踢足球	to play football
比赛	match	打网球	to play tennis
运动	sports	打乒乓	to play ping pong

我喜欢踢足球。 **I like playing football.**
他不喜欢跑步。 **He doesn't like running .**

MONTHS AND WEEK

星期一	Monday	一月	January	七月	July
星期二	Tuesday	二月	February	八月	August
星期三	Wednesday	三月	March	九月	September
星期四	Thursday	四月	April	十月	October
星期五	Friday	五月	May	十一月	November
星期六	Saturday	六月	June	十二月	December
星期天	Sunday				

MY DAY

起床	to get up	吃饭	to eat food
睡觉	to sleep	早饭	breakfast
上学	to start school	午饭	lunch
放学	to finish school	晚饭	supper

你几点起床？ **What time do you get up?**
我八点起床。 **I get up at 8 o'clock.**

43

PLACES IN CHINA

上海　Shanghai
香港　Hong Kong
黄河　Yellow River

PLACES IN CHINA

故宫　　Forbidden City
长城　　Great Wall of China
天安门　Heaven's Gate

HOLIDAYS

假期　holidays
海　　sea
海滩　beach
饭店　hotel

USEFUL QUESTIONS

你是谁？　　　　Who are you?
你吃薯条吗？　　Are you eating chips?
你要踢足球吗？　Do you want to play football?
星期几？　　　　What day is it?
几月？　　　　　Which month is it?
你去哪里？　　　Where are you going?

USEFUL ANSWERS

我们是学生。　We are students.
她吃薯条。　　She is eating chips.
我要踢足球。　I want to play football.
星期六。　　　It's Saturday.
十二月。　　　It's December.
他去上海。　　He is going to Shanghai.